A GIFT FOR:
FROM:

Published by Hallmark Gift Books,
a division of Hallmark Cards, Inc.,
Kansas City, MO 64141
Visit us on the Web at Hallmark.com.

Editorial Director: Delia Berrigan
Editor: Nate Barbarick
Art Director: Chris Opheim
Designer: Scott Swanson
Production Designer: Bryan Ring

ISBN: 978-1-59530-901-3
BOK2163

Printed and bound in China
AUG14

BE GOOD OR BE BAD
ON YOUR BIRTHDAY

WRITTEN BY SUZANNE HEINS

Hallmark

IF YOU FALL INTO SOME

CRAZY ADVENTURE..

IT'S YOUR SPECIAL DAY!
SING, CELEBRATE, AND HAVE FUN.

OR WISELY USE THE TIME TO CATCH UP ON YOUR **DIABOLICAL PLOTTING.**

WHEN IT COMES TO WHAT MAKES YOU HAPPY, YOU DESERVE THE PICK OF THE LITTER...

SUSHI?

HOPE YOUR DAY'S FULL OF ADVENTURE
AND OPPORTUNITIES TO LEARN, GROW, AND CHANGE.

OR EVEN BETTER—OPPORTUNITIES TO BE COMPLIMENTED, WAITED ON, AND WORSHIPPED.

BIRTHDAYS ARE PERFECT FOR DREAMING NEW DREAMS.

ANY DAY IS PERFECT FOR SETTLING OLD SCORES.

TODAY'S ALL ABOUT ADVENTURE
BIG WISHES, AND NOTHING BUT FUN

A BAD CROWD CAN SURE BE A GOOD TIME!

IT'S YOUR DAY!

STEP OUT OF YOUR COMFORT KINGDOM. WALK ON THE WILD SIDE. LAUGH IN THE FACE OF DANGER.

ESPECIALLY IF IT MEANS GETTING INTO SOMEONE'S HAIR.

SPREAD YOUR WINGS AND SOAR!

YEAH! SHAKE THINGS UP!

MAKE SURE YOU HAVE A VOICE IN HOW YOU CELEBRATE YOUR SPECIAL DAY.

ON THE OTHER TENTACLE,
DON'T UNDERESTIMATE THE POWER OF BODY LANGUAGE.

HAVE THE KIND OF FUN THAT ONLY COMES ALONG
ONCE IN NINE LIVES!

AND REMEMBER: THERE'S MORE THAN ONE WAY TO SKIN A CAT.

IT'S YOUR SPECIAL DAY, SO RELAX!
TAKE SOME TIME TO SIT ON THE SHELF...THINK
INSIDE THE BOX...RECHARGE YOUR BATTERIES.

**SIGHTSEE WITH PALS
ALL OVER THE KINGDOM!**

KICK BACK, RELAX
AND TAKE IT EASY ON YOUR BIRTHDAY.

OR FREAK OUT

ABOUT BEING ANOTHER YEAR OLDER.

OH PLEASE, OH PLEASE, OH PLEASE, HAVE A DAY FILLED WITH ALL KINDS OF UPLIFTING FUN.

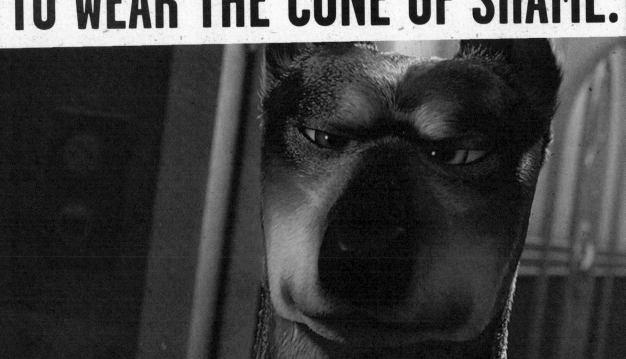

HAVE ONE OF THE HAPPIEST DAYS
IN THE WESTERN WORLD...OR IN THE ENTIRE GALAXY!

IT'S YOUR SPECIAL DAY! SO WHAT WILL IT BE: CELEBRATING WITH SOME FINE DINING?

If you have enjoyed this book
or it has touched your life in some way,
we would love to hear from you.

Please send your comments to:
Hallmark Book Feedback
P.O. Box 419034
Mail Drop 100
Kansas City, MO 64141

Or e-mail us at:
booknotes@hallmark.com